CAT

M000083037

Circle the letter in play.

A B C D E F G H I J K L M N O P Q R S T U V W X Y Z

FICTIONAL CHARACTER	FRUIT	COUNTRY
TELEVISION SHOW	SILLY THING	FOUND IN AN OFFICE
SONG TITLE	ANIMAL	DESSERT

Circle the letter in play.

A B C D E F G H I J K L M N O P Q R S T U V W X Y Z

CARTOON CHARACTER	VEGETABLE	CITY
CELEBRITY	ANNOYING THING	FOUND IN A KITCHEN
MOVIE TITLE	OCCUPATION	GAME

CATEGORIES

Circle the letter in play.

A B C D E F G H I J K L M N O P Q R S T U V W X Y Z

FICTIONAL CHARACTER	FRUIT	COUNTRY
TELEVISION SHOW	SILLY THING	FOUND IN AN OFFICE
SONG TITLE	ANIMAL	DESSERT

Circle the letter in play.

A B C D E F G H I J K L M N O P Q R S T U V W X Y Z

CARTOON CHARACTER	VEGETABLE	CITY
CELEBRITY	ANNOYING THING	FOUND IN A KITCHEN
MOVIE TITLE	OCCUPATION	GAME

CATEGORIES

FICTIONAL CHARACTER	FRUIT	COUNTRY
TELEVISION SHOW	SILLY THING	FOUND IN AN OFFICE
SONG TITLE	ANIMAL	DESSERT

CARTOON CHARACTER	VEGETABLE	CITY
CELEBRITY	ANNOYING THING	FOUND IN A KITCHEN
MOVIE TITLE	OCCUPATION	GAME

CATEGORIES

Circle the letter in play.
A B C D E F G H I J K L M N O P Q R S T U V W X Y Z

FICTIONAL CHARACTER	FRUIT	COUNTRY
TELEVISION SHOW	SILLY THING	FOUND IN AN OFFICE
SONG TITLE	ANIMAL	DESSERT

Circle the letter in play.

A B C D E F G H I J K L M N O P Q R S T U V W X Y Z

CARTOON CHARACTER	VEGETABLE	CITY
CELEBRITY	ANNOYING THING	FOUND IN A KITCHEN
MOVIE TITLE	OCCUPATION	GAME

CATEGORIES

Circle the letter in play.

A B C D E F G H I J K L M N O P Q R S T U V W X Y Z

FICTIONAL CHARACTER	FRUIT	COUNTRY
TELEVISION SHOW	SILLY THING	FOUND IN AN OFFICE
SONG TITLE	ANIMAL	DESSERT

Circle the letter in play.

A B C D E F G H I J K L M N O P Q R S T U V W X Y Z

CARTOON CHARACTER	VEGETABLE	CITY
CELEBRITY	ANNOYING THING	FOUND IN A KITCHEN
MOVIE TITLE	OCCUPATION	GAME

CATEGORIES

Circle the letter in play.

A B C D E F G H I J K L M N O P Q R S T U V W X Y Z

FICTIONAL CHARACTER	FRUIT	COUNTRY
TELEVISION SHOW	SILLY THING	FOUND IN AN OFFICE
SONG TITLE	ANIMAL	DESSERT

Circle the letter in play.

A B C D E F G H I J K L M N O P Q R S T U V W X Y Z

CARTOON CHARACTER	VEGETABLE	CITY
CELEBRITY	ANNOYING THING	FOUND IN A KITCHEN
MOVIE TITLE	OCCUPATION	GAME

CATEGORIES

Circle the letter in play.

A B C D E F G H I J K L M N O P Q R S T U V W X Y Z

FICTIONAL CHARACTER	FRUIT	COUNTRY
TELEVISION SHOW	SILLY THING	FOUND IN AN OFFICE
SONG TITLE	ANIMAL	DESSERT

Circle the letter in play.

A B C D E F G H I J K L M N O P Q R S T U V W X Y Z

CARTOON CHARACTER	VEGETABLE	CITY
CELEBRITY	ANNOYING THING	FOUND IN A KITCHEN
MOVIE TITLE	OCCUPATION	GAME

CATEGORIES

A B C D E F G H I J K L M N O P Q R S T U V W X Y Z

FICTIONAL CHARACTER	FRUIT	COUNTRY
TELEVISION SHOW	SILLY THING	FOUND IN AN OFFICE
SONG TITLE	ANIMAL	DESSERT

A B C D E F G H I J K L M N O P Q R S T U V W X Y Z

CARTOON CHARACTER	VEGETABLE	CITY
CELEBRITY	ANNOYING THING	FOUND IN A KITCHEN
MOVIE TITLE	OCCUPATION	GAME

CATEGORIES

Circle the letter in play.

A B C D E F G H I J K L M N O P Q R S T U V W X Y Z

FICTIONAL CHARACTER	FRUIT	COUNTRY
TELEVISION SHOW	SILLY THING	FOUND IN AN OFFICE
SONG TITLE	ANIMAL	DESSERT

Circle the letter in play.

A B C D E F G H I J K L M N O P Q R S T U V W X Y Z

CARTOON CHARACTER	VEGETABLE	CITY
CELEBRITY	ANNOYING THING	FOUND IN A KITCHEN
MOVIE TITLE	OCCUPATION	GAME

CATEGORIES

Circle the letter in play.

A B C D E F G H I J K L M N O P Q R S T U V W X Y Z

FICTIONAL CHARACTER	FRUIT	COUNTRY
TELEVISION SHOW	SILLY THING	FOUND IN AN OFFICE
SONG TITLE	ANIMAL	DESSERT

Circle the letter in play.

A B C D E F G H I J K L M N O P Q R S T U V W X Y Z

CARTOON CHARACTER	VEGETABLE	CITY
CELEBRITY	ANNOYING THING	FOUND IN A KITCHEN
MOVIE TITLE	OCCUPATION	GAME

CATEGORIES

Circle the letter in play.

A B C D E F G H I J K L M N O P Q R S T U V W X Y Z

FICTIONAL CHARACTER	FRUIT	COUNTRY
TELEVISION SHOW	SILLY THING	FOUND IN AN OFFICE
SONG TITLE	ANIMAL	DESSERT

Circle the letter in play.

A B C D E F G H I J K L M N O P Q R S T U V W X Y Z

CARTOON CHARACTER	VEGETABLE	CITY
CELEBRITY	ANNOYING THING	FOUND IN A KITCHEN
MOVIE TITLE	OCCUPATION	GAME

TIC-TAC-TOE

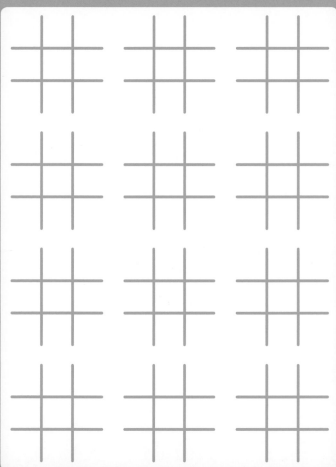

TIC-TAC-TOE

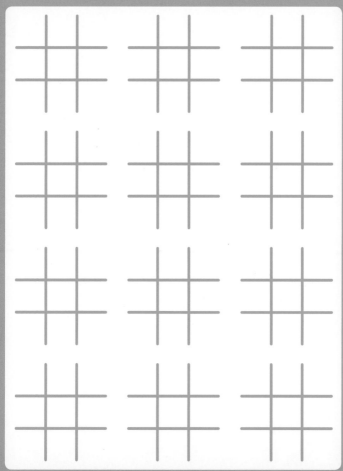

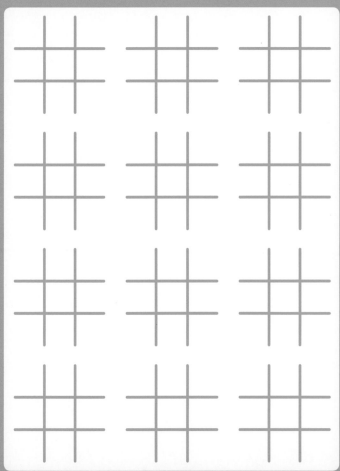

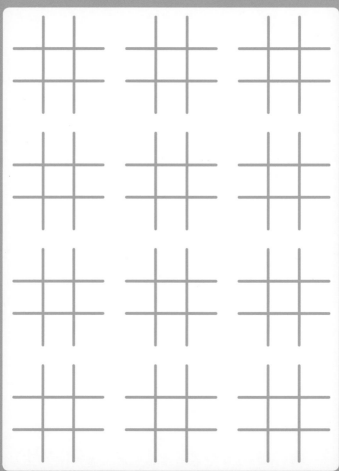

TIC-TAC-TOE

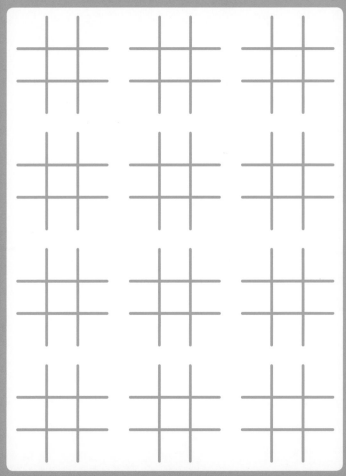

TIC-TAC-TOE

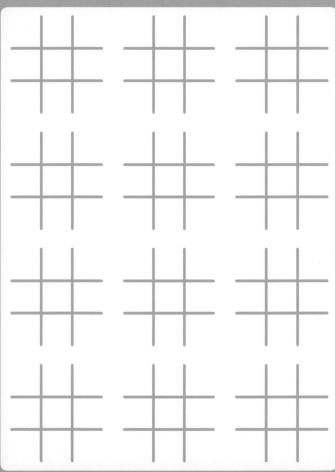

TIC-TAC-TOE

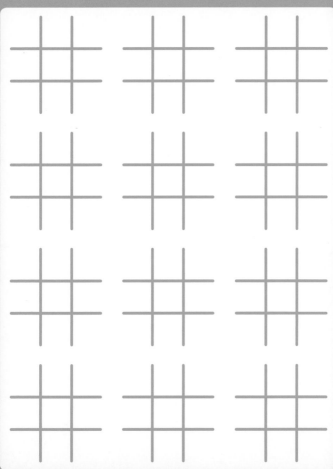

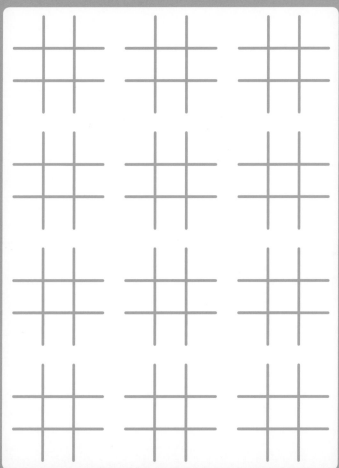

TIC-TAC-TOE

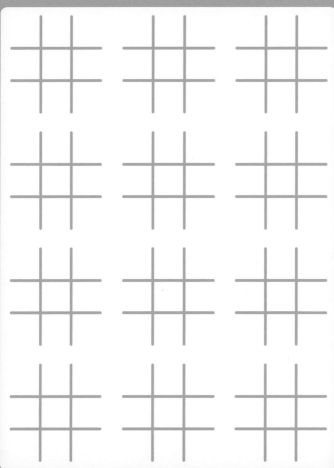

TIC-TAC-TOE

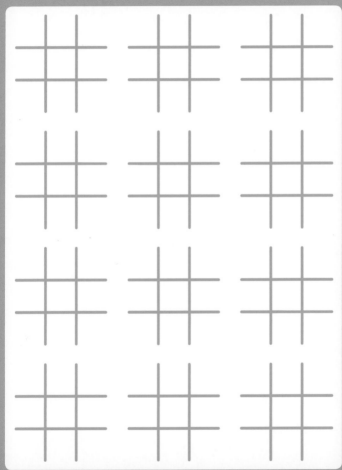

TIC-TAC-TOE

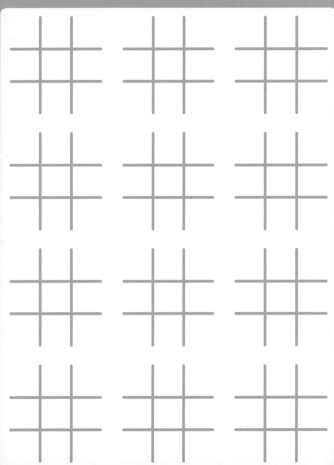

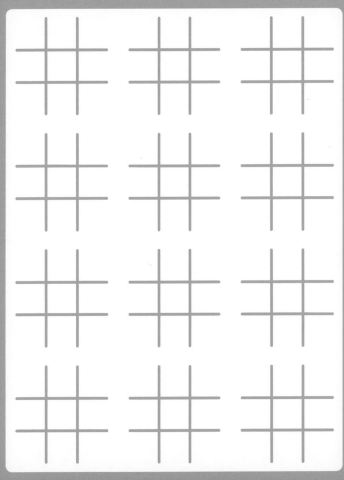

TIC-TAC-TOE

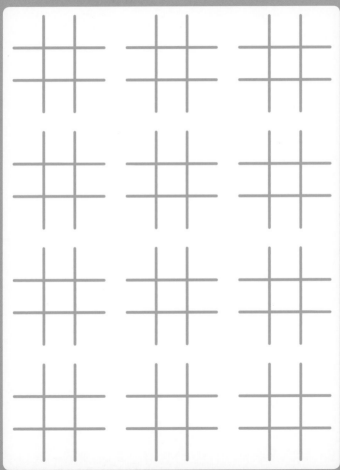

TIC-TAC-TOE

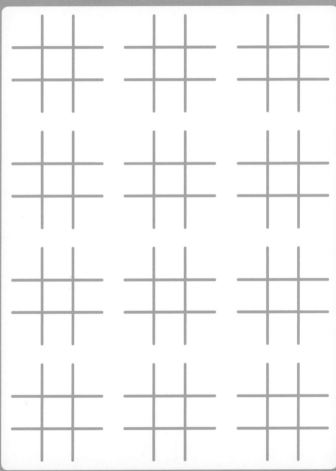

TIC-TAC-TOE

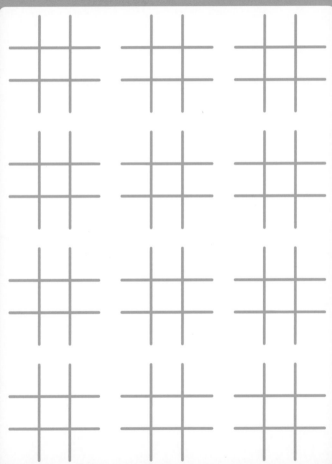

CONNECT 5

CONNECT 5

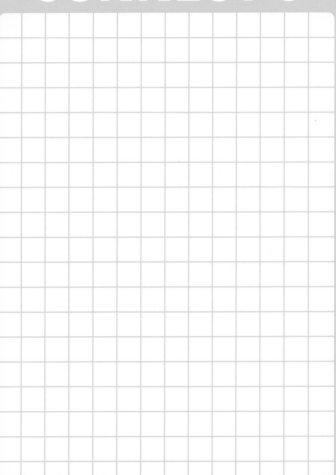

CONNECT 5

CONNECT 5

CONNECT 5

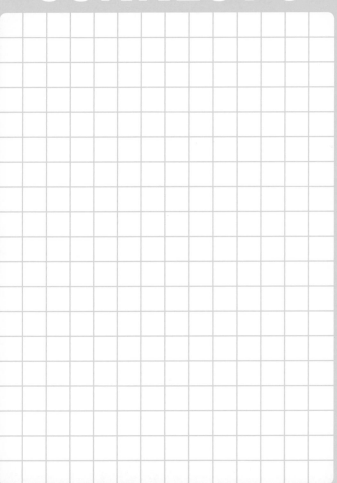

CONNECT 5

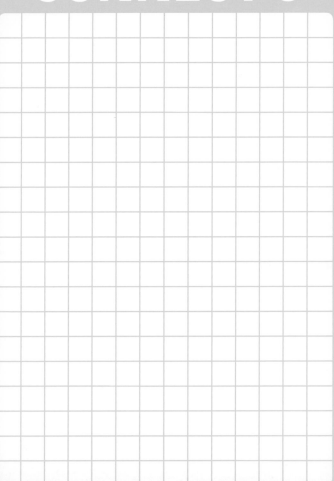

CONNECT 5

CONNECT 5

CONNECT 5

CONNECT 5

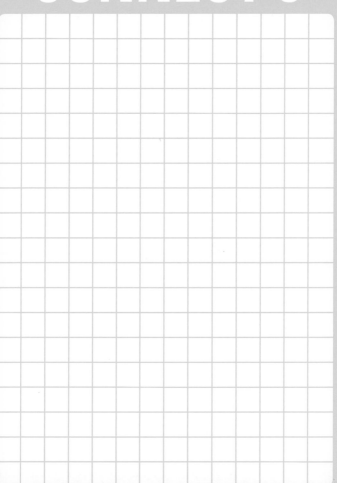

CONNECT 5

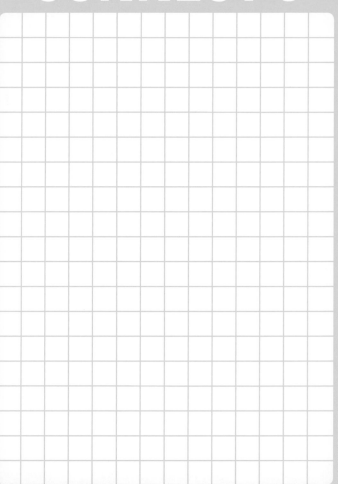

CONNECT 5

CONNECT 5

CONNECT 5